ACTION GUIDE for DIVERSITY BEYOND LIP SERVICE

LA'WANA HARRIS

Library of Congress Control Number: 2019902523

Customization and Bulk sales: Special discounts are available on customizable bulk purchases by corporations, associations, and others. For details, contact the author at coachlawana@gmail.com.

Photo Credits: Pixabay, Pexels
Page 14: © Photographerlondon | Dreamstime.com
Page 19: © Sam74100 | Dreamstime.com
Page 26: © Kantver | Dreamstime.com
Page 37: © Kantver | Dreamstime.com
Page 67: © s4svisuals | Adobe Stock
Page 78: © Gotstock | Dreamstime.com
Page 79: © VadimGuzhva | Adobe Stock
Page 85: © luckybusiness | Adobe Stock

Printed in the United States of America

When it is available, we choose paper that has been manufactured by environmentally responsible processes. These may include using trees grown in sustainable forests, incorporating recycled paper, minimizing chlorine in bleaching, or recycling the energy produced at the paper mill.

Introduction 5

The COMMIT Model 10

Commit to Courageous Action 14

Open Your Eyes and Ears 26

Move Beyond Lip Service 37

Make Room for Controversy and Conflict 48

Invite New Perspectives 61

Tell the Truth Even When it Hurts 74

Ready to Commit? 94

Additional Resources 97

Introduction

We've spent decades telling people what they should think, say, and do relative to diversity and inclusion. It's what I call "D&I from the outside-in."

In *Diversity Beyond Lip Service*, I proposed a novel "inside-out" approach called Inclusion Coaching that encourages individuals to first go deep within to own where they are and embrace their truth, relative to diversity and inclusion. It is only then they can do the **self-work** needed to move forward on their diversity and inclusion journey.

This *Action Guide* is designed as a **companion** to ***Diversity Beyond Lip Service*** to help you, your team, and your organization with the everyday actions that create inclusive cultures. While this guide can stand alone as a starting point for your diversity and inclusion journey, I believe your experience in taking action and exploring your own truths will be deeper and more fruitful if you first read ***Diversity Beyond Lip Service***.

Creating inclusive cultures requires that everyone be on board, and so throughout the guide I will show how you can do your part to ensure that **all voices are heard and valued** in your organization's conversation—regardless of where you fall in the power structure. Former clients, contributors, and colleagues have graciously lent their voices and insights to the discussion, although names and companies have been changed for those who prefer to remain anonymous.

INCLUSION COACHING AND THE COMMIT MODEL

Coaching for inclusion is a powerful way to overcome diversity and inclusion (D&I) resistance because it starts by engaging individuals where they are without judgment. For example, instead of being told at a traditional D&I training session that you need to be "more inclusive" and to make sure everyone can recite your D&I policy, Inclusion Coaching supports you in facing your own biases and resistance in a safe space in order to break them down and move toward a more inclusive mindset and, consequently, more inclusive actions.

The COMMIT coaching model brings structure to the Inclusion Coaching process by providing a framework for building a mindset and environment where inclusion can thrive.

Commit to Courageous Action (for self, team, organization, industry)
Open Your Eyes and Ears (to the good, the bad, and the ugly)
Move Beyond Lip Service
Make Room for Controversy and Conflict
Invite New Perspectives
Tell the Truth Even When it Hurts

While the six steps sound (and are) simple, they are not necessarily easy. For a deeper dive into Inclusion Coaching and the COMMIT Model, I encourage you to read *Diversity Beyond Lip Service: A Coaching Guide for Challenging Bias*. You can also visit lawanaharris.com for additional information and resources.

How to use this Action Guide

A few prompts are included in this guide to help you embrace a coaching mindset and practice the core concepts shared in ***Diversity Beyond Lip Service.***

Gain insights to help you engage in D&I at a deeper level.	ENGAGE
Lean into your curiosity and expand awareness of diverse perspectives.	LISTEN
Go deep within to reflect on where you are and where you want to go.	REFLECT
Select a few actions to apply for yourself, others, and your organization.	APPLY
Commit to courageous action to advance diversity, equity, inclusion, and belonging.	COMMIT

START WHERE YOU ARE

This Action Guide is not meant to be linear or prescriptive. We are all at different stages in our D&I journey, and so it is important to start where you are, with whichever step resonates the most with you. You decide where and how you engage based on your needs.

I encourage you to challenge your assumptions and remain open to whatever shows up as you work through the assessments, actions, and reflections. Give yourself the space to understand your truth when it comes to privilege without feeling pressured to feel any specific way. It is only from that point of self-actualization, vulnerability, and humility that we can build a path forward—together.

Last but not least, please remember to celebrate your successes along the way as you take steps toward increasing inclusion at your organization and in your life. Every action matters.

Three Core Principles of Inclusion Coaching

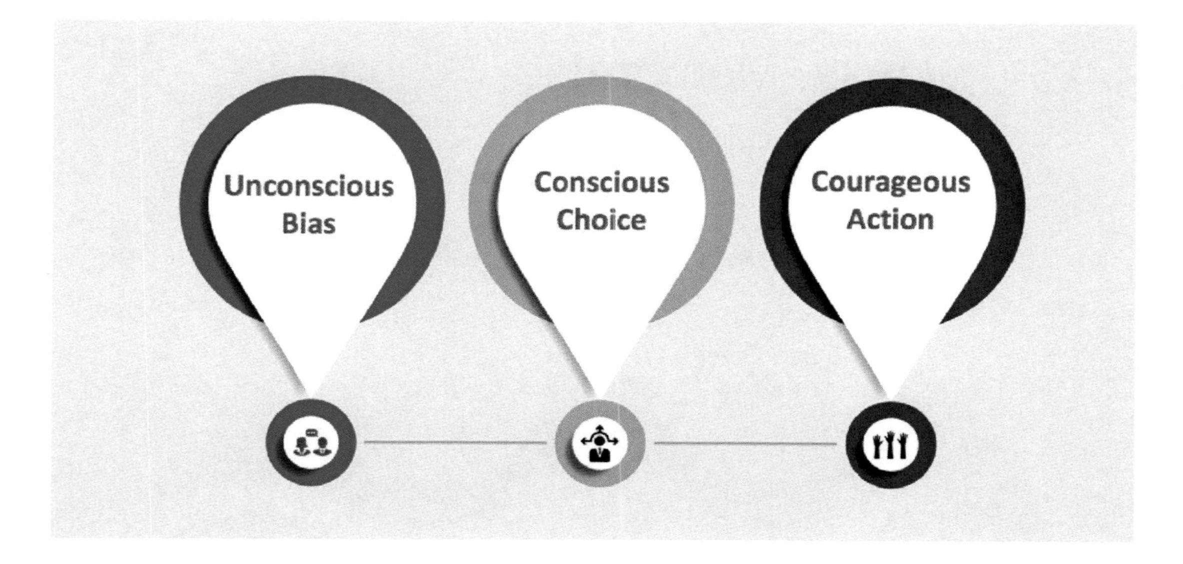

No organization is immune to the complex issues that can arise when people of different backgrounds and experiences work together. Inclusion Coaching helps to resolve these issues by focusing on three core principles:

Unconscious bias: What are my thoughts and beliefs that unwittingly marginalize or discriminate against diverse groups?

Conscious choice: What choices am I making day in and day out toward creating and upholding a welcoming and inclusive workplace culture?

Courageous action: How can I respectfully challenge and call out biases, rather than relying on higher-ups or HR representatives to handle these situations?

The COMMIT Model

Simple, Memorable, Actionable

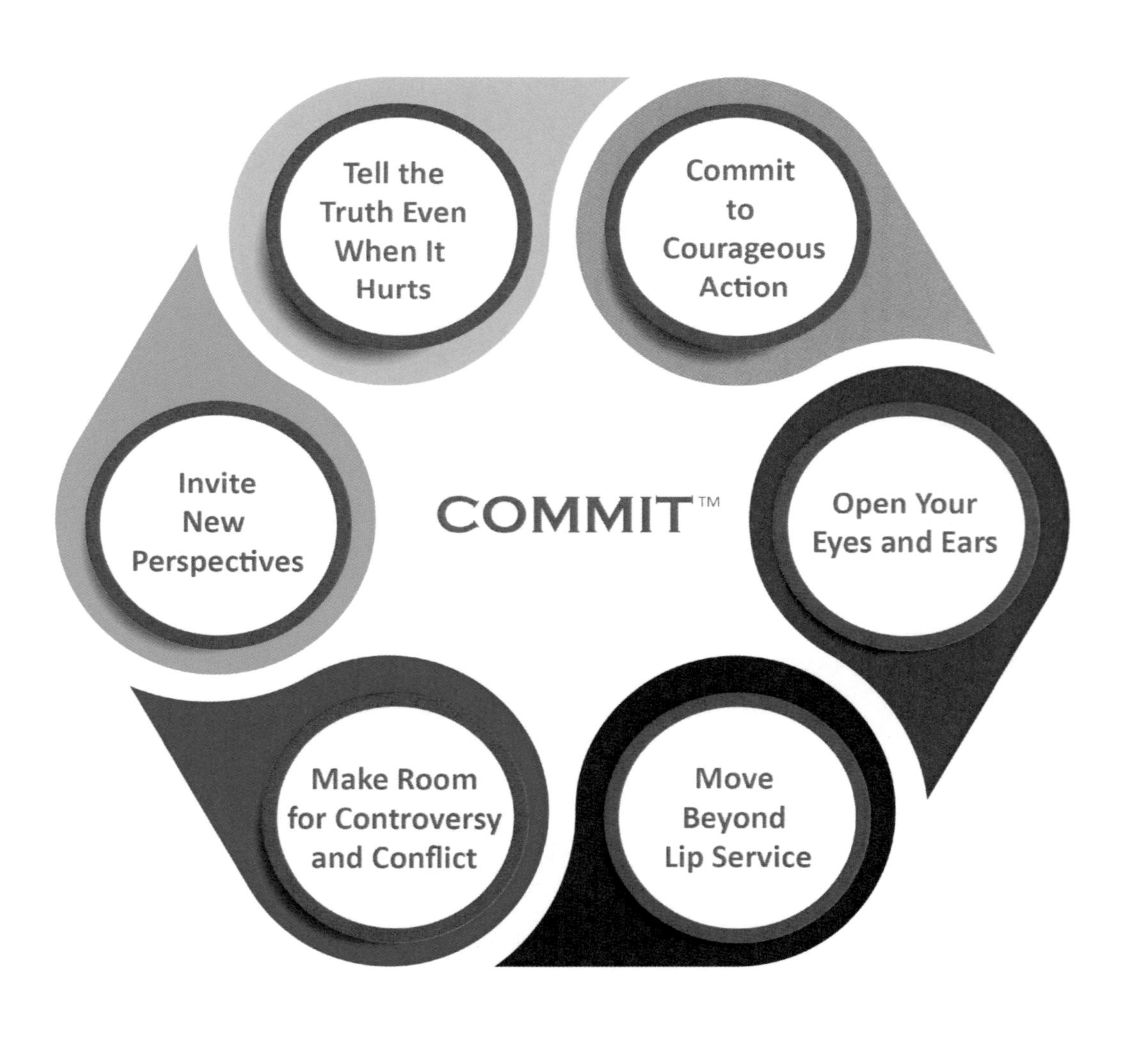

STICKINESS

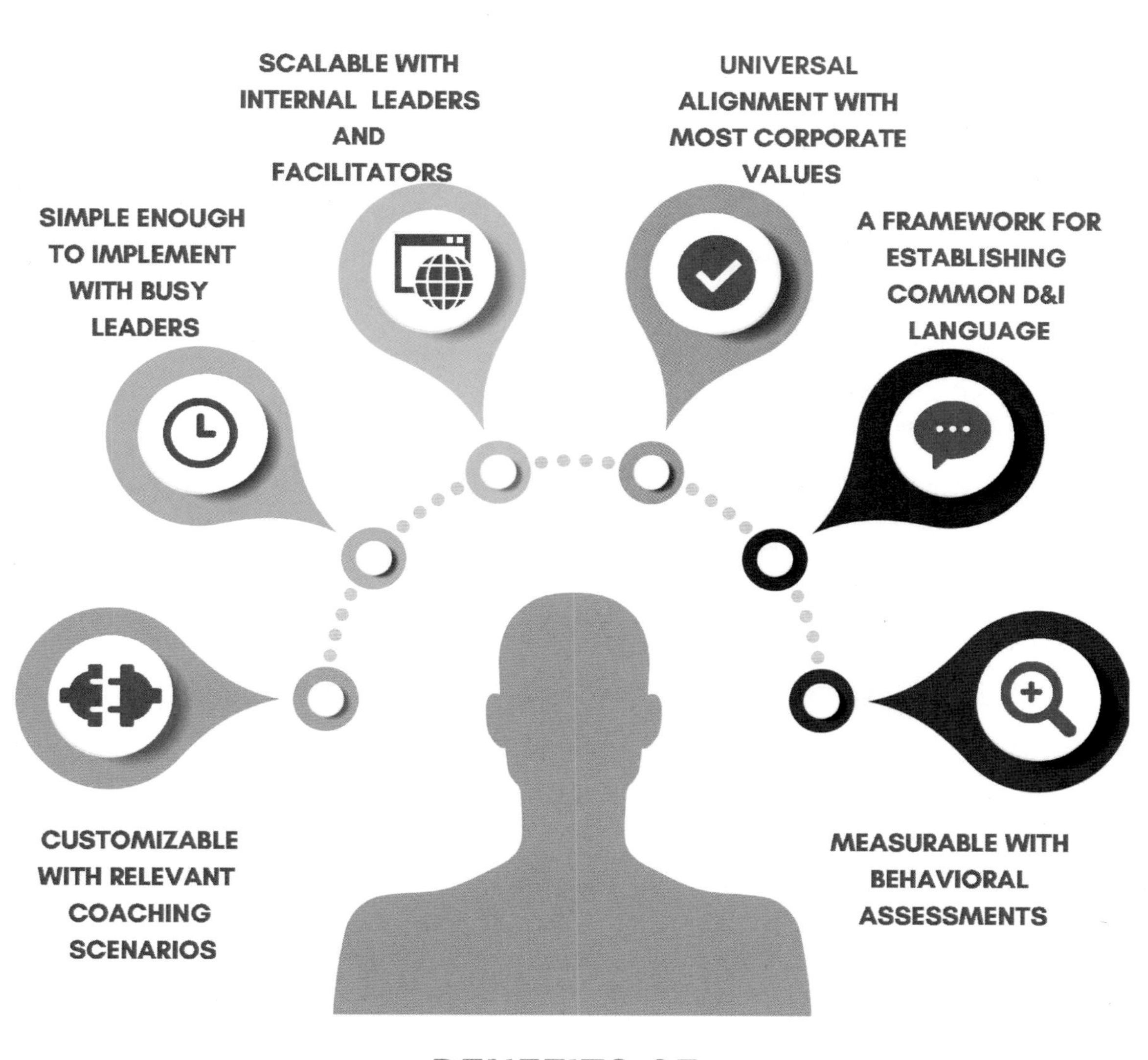

BENEFITS OF INCLUSION COACHING AND THE COMMIT MODEL

INCLUSION CIRCLE

Inclusion Circles™ are group meetings that serve as a circle of trust for unfiltered dialogue where people can learn and grow together.

In an Inclusion Circle™, diverse group members are invited to talk about their positive experiences, painful moments, wishes, feelings, and overall thoughts and insights on working toward diversity and inclusion. Each participant is encouraged to repeat back to the speaker what they heard that person say, to be sure they are really listening deeply and engaging in a transformative dialogue without judgment. Interruption, cross talk, and responding with personal opinions are avoided.

INCLUSIVE LEADERSHIP BEHAVIORS

Leaders must look in the mirror and be honest about what they see.

Practices self-reflection and mindfulness
Embraces Servant Leadership
Demonstrates an openness to different ways of thinking, doing, and being
Displays vulnerability by owning their shortcomings and mistakes
Listens to understand
Demonstrates a sharing of power for the betterment of all
Values the inherent worth of every person
Creates safe spaces for exploration, creativity, and risk-taking
Is intentional about learning and unlearning
Exhibits strong cross-cultural competency
Displays courage by standing up for others
Is equally concerned about people and business
Acknowledges intersectionality and that there is diversity within diversity
Effectively manages each individual's needs in addition to the team as a unit
Ensures that conflicts are resolved in ways that leave all team members feeling respected and heard
Gives actionable feedback and support to help others achieve their goals
Creates a culture of belonging for all
Displays interpersonal integrity (makes decisions and interacts with people in a consistent manner)
Solicits feedback relative to their blind spots and biases
Consistently honors their values

C

DIVERSITY BEYOND LIP SERVICE

ENGAGE

The workplace is not society-proof; the issues affecting society don't go away when we clock in. Diversity and inclusion professionals work hard to inspire ways to **confront** this **reality**.

Unfortunately, these efforts can be co-opted, leading to a series of discussions, events, and initiatives that merely assemble diverse groups of people for conversations or limited, surface-level concessions rather than practically improve their experiences.

An initiative to hire more people of color or install access ramps for employees with disabilities is admirable; however, the initiatives by themselves do not create an inclusive workplace.

For example, increasing the diversity of your workforce is a great goal to work toward, but it does more harm than good to hire marginalized groups of people into an environment unprepared to receive them.

We are at a critical juncture between **good intentions** and a **still-less- than-ideal reality**.

It's time to **go beyond** presenting the business case, building awareness, and training in unconscious bias. It's time to go courageously into new territory: deep into the root causes of D&I resistance that are preventing real inclusion from taking seed in the workplace.

Our lives begin to end the day we
become silent about the things that matter.
Dr. Martin Luther King Jr.

Courage is the most
important
of all the virtues,
because without courage
you can't practice any other virtue
consistently.
You can practice any virtue
erratically, but nothing consistently
without courage.

Maya Angelou

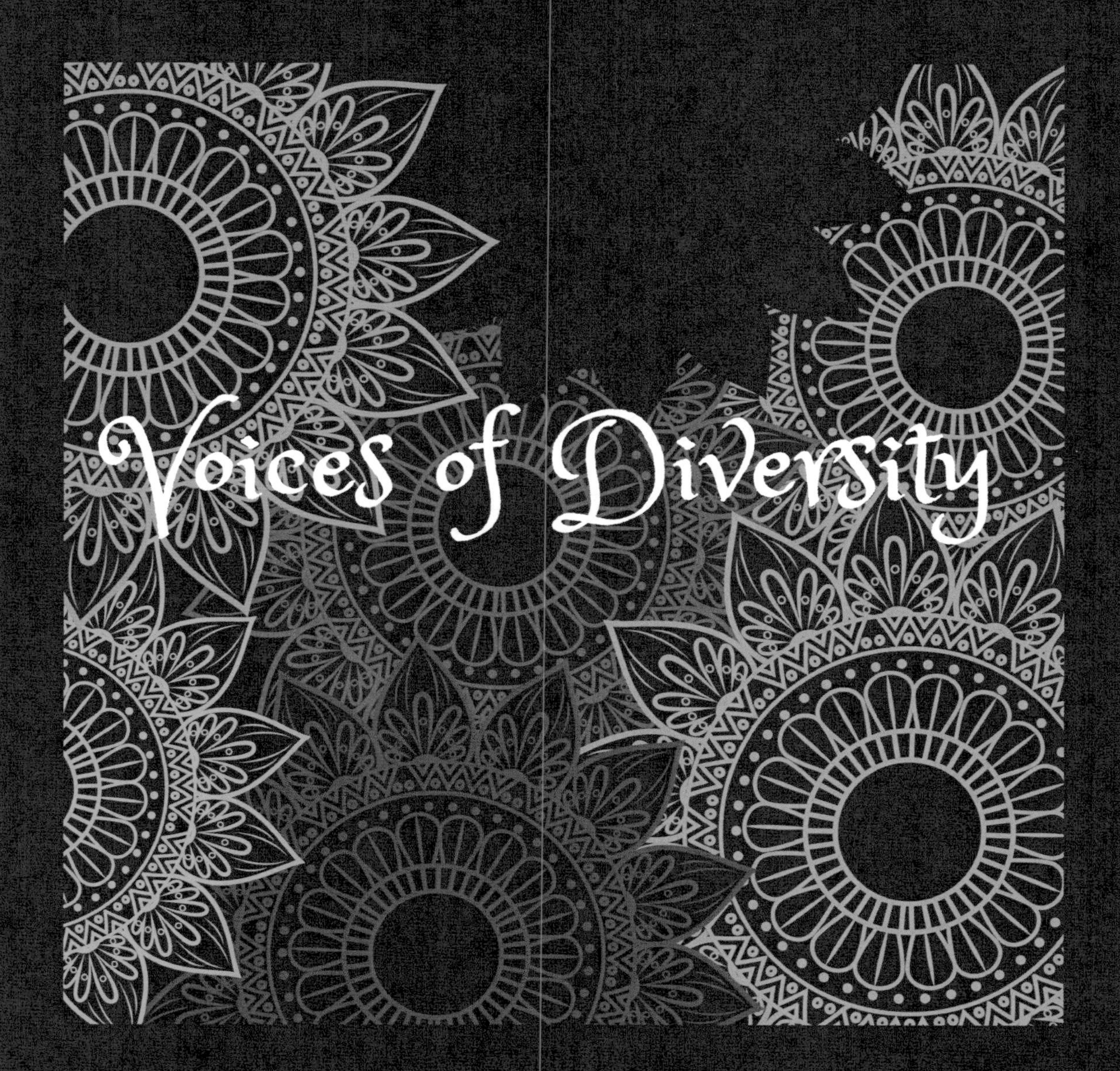
Voices of Diversity

MILLENNIAL PERSPECTIVE

Here's the thing, we actually paid attention. We listened when we were being spoken to and when we weren't. You were telling us the best things you knew based on your life experiences.

Here are a few examples.

"You go to work because you must. If you love what you do, it's a huge bonus; however, most people only enjoy components of their job." Truth. We watched you drag yourself to work for years only to come home and complain about every facet of the day- except the occasional, comedic moment with your coworker or slither of appreciation from upper management. We were not about to sign up for that. Especially when we also listened to your account of the "dream that got away". You know the story. It always starts with some moment in your youth when you decided to go down the path you now regret. We understand the practicality of securing a job so that you survive. However, we are not interested in building a life on that premise.

Most parents have given some version of the success talk. "If you do well in school and work hard, you will get a decent job and have success. You will be an educated, professional with a consistent income. Maybe you'll be able to afford a new car in a few years and a mortgage in a couple more years after that. You'll get married, start a family, and after working 40 years—you'll be able to retire. Sounds like the dream, right?" Wrong!

Like many of my friends, I graduated, took a corporate job, relocated and moved into my corporate apartment. The company set up my corporate devices, issued my corporate credit card and delivered my company car. I'd receive a weekly itinerary message for flight information and car rental details. I was in many ways quickly climbing the success ladder. Until I realized that I hated my job. I had money, stability and some semblance of social approval and I was miserable.

The map was clear and accurate, but not for my generation. We need a new map to help us navigate to new destinations- a map that leads to what our generation wants and needs—to make a difference. We don't want the empty promise of happiness nor it's evil twin, apathetic complacency. We want the magic we were told to long for. We want to live our dream life in the real world.

COURAGE

75% of millennials would take a pay cut to work for a socially responsible company.

2016 Cone Communication Study

TOMORROW'S LEADERS ARE LOOKING FOR MORE THAN A PAYCHECK.

THEY ARE EVALUATING THE SOCIAL CONSCIOUSNESS OF PROSPECTIVE ORGANIZATIONS.

HOW WILL YOU COACH THE NEXT GENERATION OF LEADERS?

How Will You Coach The Next Generation of Leaders To Commit To Courageous Action?

The COMMIT Model guides coaches in asking individuals empowering questions that tap into their truths and ignite their curiosity about themselves and those who are different from them.

SAMPLE COACHING QUESTIONS:

What is the difference you want to make to D&I efforts?

What are you committed to doing relative to D&I?

What does success look like and how will you measure it?

How can you create a culture of inclusion?

What will you do? By when?

CREATE YOUR OWN COURAGEOUS ACTION COACHING QUESTIONS:

____

____

____

____

____

Assessment

RATE EACH STATEMENT USING THE FOLLOWING:

5 Strongly Agree
4 Agree
3 Neutral
2 Disagree
1 Strongly Disagree

I am committed to taking action to improve inclusion. _______

I set expectations and specific goals for inclusivity with my team while modeling inclusive behaviors. _______

I advocate for inclusion as a corporate value and core leadership competency. _______

I create and act on ways to build a culture of inclusion. ______

I "walk the talk" of inclusion by treating everyone with dignity and respect. ______

What are your areas of strength? How have they shown up in your life?

____

____

What are your areas of opportunity? How have they shown up in your life?

____

____

APPLICATION

SELF

- Identify your strengths and opportunities with the COMMIT self-assessment.
- Create an action plan to amplify your strengths and develop in your areas of opportunity.
- Share your plans with your manager and benchmark your progress.

TEAM

- Integrate the The COMMIT model into your employee coaching discussions.
- Encourage your team to take the COMMIT self-assessment and identify their strengths and areas of opportunity.
- Create a safe space for team members to share their strengths and weaknesses.

BUSINESS

- Join or take a leadership role in an ERG/BRG or Inclusion Council to help identify synergies with business needs.
- Identify ways that D&I can enable your business imperatives.
- Incorporate D&I metrics in your business plan.

REFLECTION

What comes up for you as you reflect on this question?

Capture your thoughts in the notes section.

Notes

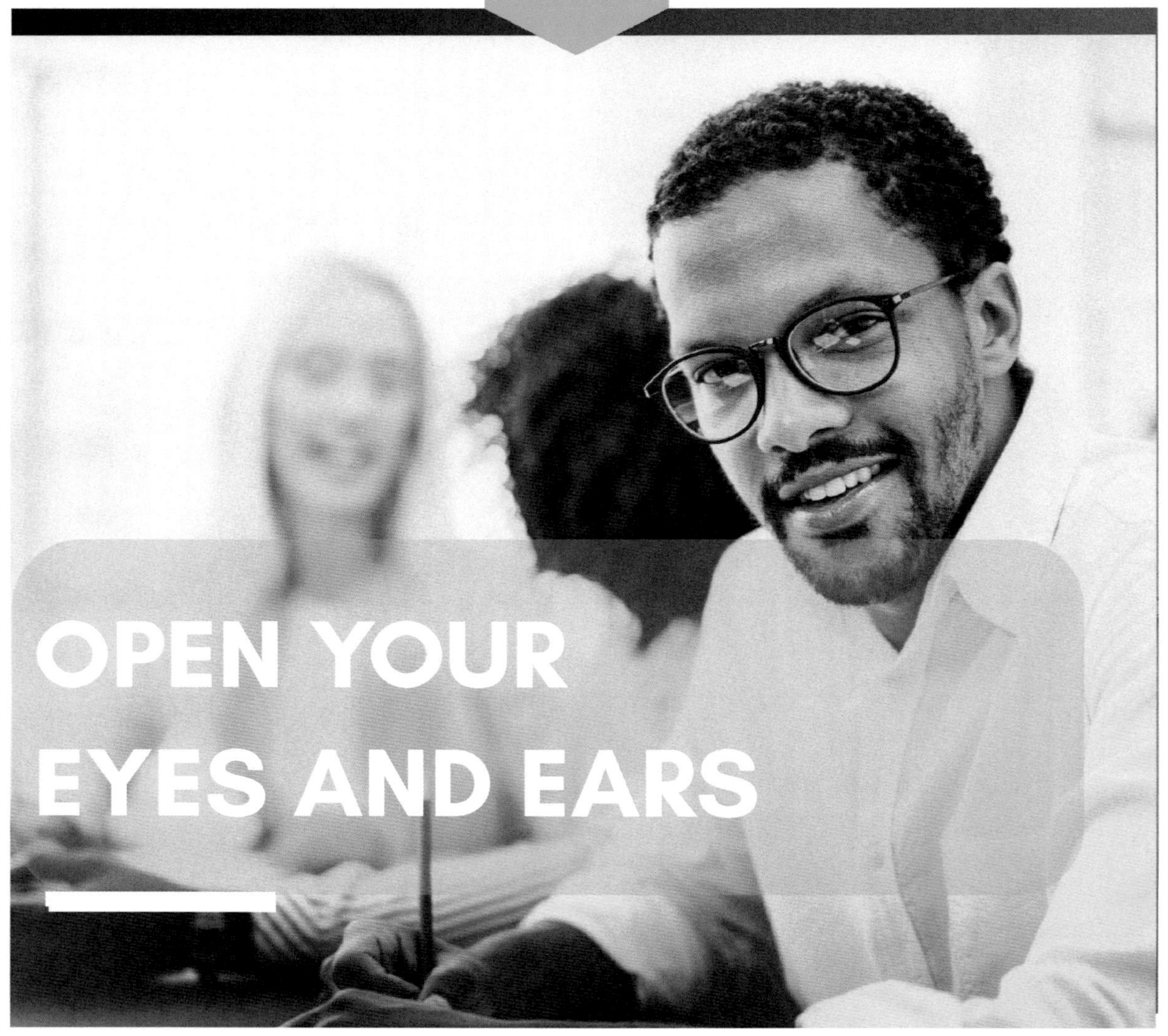

DIVERSITY BEYOND LIP SERVICE

QUOTABLES

*Coaching unleashes
the radical truth
and transformative power
that lies dormant
within each of us.*

One major impediment to achieving a "welcoming, collaborative, and thriving environment" is a widespread tendency to neither see nor hear the ways in which diversity group members are subjected to subtle discrimination and microaggressions, which cumulatively nullify both their individuality and their humanity.

Microaggressions are subtle comments or actions that demonstrate bias against an individual from a marginalized group. Whether intentional or not, these instances, which often masquerade as good intentions, or worse, enlightenment, perpetuate inequality.

Microaggressions can feel like water dripping on a rock—eventually wearing down even the strongest person if left unchecked.

To avoid them, many people choose to wear a mask at work, embracing their authentic self and culture only after they close the door to their office on their way out for the day. Others decide to leave an organization entirely to find a workplace where they don't have to compromise or hide their identity.

By making the effort to see and hear the subtle and covert, as well as the obvious and overt, the two forms that deeply ingrained biases and discriminatory tendencies take, you remove the corresponding cultural veil of denial and avoidance.

Voices of Diversity

WHITE, MALE, GAY, PROGRESSIVE - WOKE

The "bad people" propagate racism and male chauvinism. I've always distinguished myself from "those people" with "not me" rationalizations: not me, my family worked hard just to make a modest living. Not me, I'm a lifelong progressive. Not me, I'm gay—one of the oppressed. Not me, I've worked to help the less fortunate. Not me, I'm a deeply empathetic person—ask anyone!

For decades, I sang myself a "not me" lullaby to maintain my comfortable slumber of denial until a confluence of events created enough noise to jar me awake. In the world around me, I was stirred by displays of newly emboldened white supremacy on the one hand, and the shocking truths exposed by the #MeToo movement on the other hand. In my professional experiences, I was prodded by a sudden and persistent pattern of (mostly young) voices raised in the workplace, challenging deeply ingrained and dangerously subtle patterns of discrimination.

My awakening began gradually until one day the shades were thrown open. I was conducting a leadership development workshop for a client. My material calls out different styles of leadership, one of which I call the "Trustworthy Citizen." The idea is to suggest that sometimes being a leader is simply about modeling behaviors of a cooperative member of the workplace community. Once I'd presented the concept, one member of the group spoke up by pointing out that the word "citizen" aligned with white supremacist rhetoric, and that she and others in the room were uncomfortable with my language. I could feel the tips of my ears burning as I attempted a reassuring reply.

"Thank you for sharing your view. That's important to hear. But let's not get hung up on my word choices; let's focus on the idea I'm trying to convey. I'm not here as a diversity expert, I'm just here to talk about leadership skills…"

My assurances did not have the effect I'd hoped for, and for a few minutes I presided over what was for me an extremely awkward and uncomfortable conversation, ending with my retreating to this: "I feel uncomfortable facilitating this conversation, especially as a middle-aged white guy."

That was it. That was the moment I fully woke up, albeit in a daze. I was fully exposed to the light of my privileged effort to escape the moment because it was uncomfortable to me. Things had turned awkward for me, and so in my position of power as the outside expert and a middle-aged white male, I was shutting it down. When I heard the suggestion that my leadership material could somehow be associated with white supremacy, I freaked out. I was panicked, guilt-ridden, and defiant all at once.

"No, not me," said my inside voice. "I'm a good guy."

I am awake and I am seeking to learn what I can do with that clarity. I'm ready to find ways to use owning the fact of my White Male Privilege as a tool for doing even more good.

Visit BraveShift.com to learn more.

Assessment

RATE EACH STATEMENT USING THE FOLLOWING:

5 Strongly Agree
4 Agree
3 Neutral
2 Disagree
1 Strongly Disagree

I practice deep listening with empathetic presence to build connections with others. _______

I recognize and manage my own blind spots, biases, and limiting beliefs.

____

I consider and address stereotypes that can affect work assignments and environments. _______

I maintain a zero-tolerance policy when confronted with oppressive, exclusionary, or prejudiced behavior at work and outside of work. ______

I recognize that privilege and systemic biases affect policies, hiring, succession planning, and promotions. ______

What are your areas of strength? How have they shown up in your life?

____

____

What are your areas of opportunity? How have they shown up in your life?

____

____

APPLICATION

SELF

- Be intentional about understanding the experience of non-majority employees.
- Establish a mentoring relationship with someone different from you.
- Tune in to the internal dialogue, preferences, and patterns that show up in your interactions with others.

TEAM

- Create a "Voices of Diversity" segment for your team meetings to increase awareness and connection.
- Establish a team charter that explicitly calls out inclusive behaviors.
- Conduct a "Stop, Start, Continue" exercise to get a pulse of where your team is relative to inclusion and belonging.

BUSINESS

- Apply a D&I lens when evaluating business prospects.
- Ensure diverse representation when making key business decisions. (Go beyond "diversity of thought.")
- Identify and own areas that are deficient in the current D&I landscape.

How Will You Coach The Next Generation of Leaders To Commit To Open Their Eyes And Ears?

The COMMIT Model guides coaches in asking individuals empowering questions that tap into their truths and ignite their curiosity about themselves and those who are different from them.

SAMPLE COACHING QUESTIONS:

What do you see?

What are you overlooking?

What can you stop tolerating?

What is it like to be you?

Who are you?

CREATE YOUR OWN COACHING QUESTIONS:

____

____

____

____

____

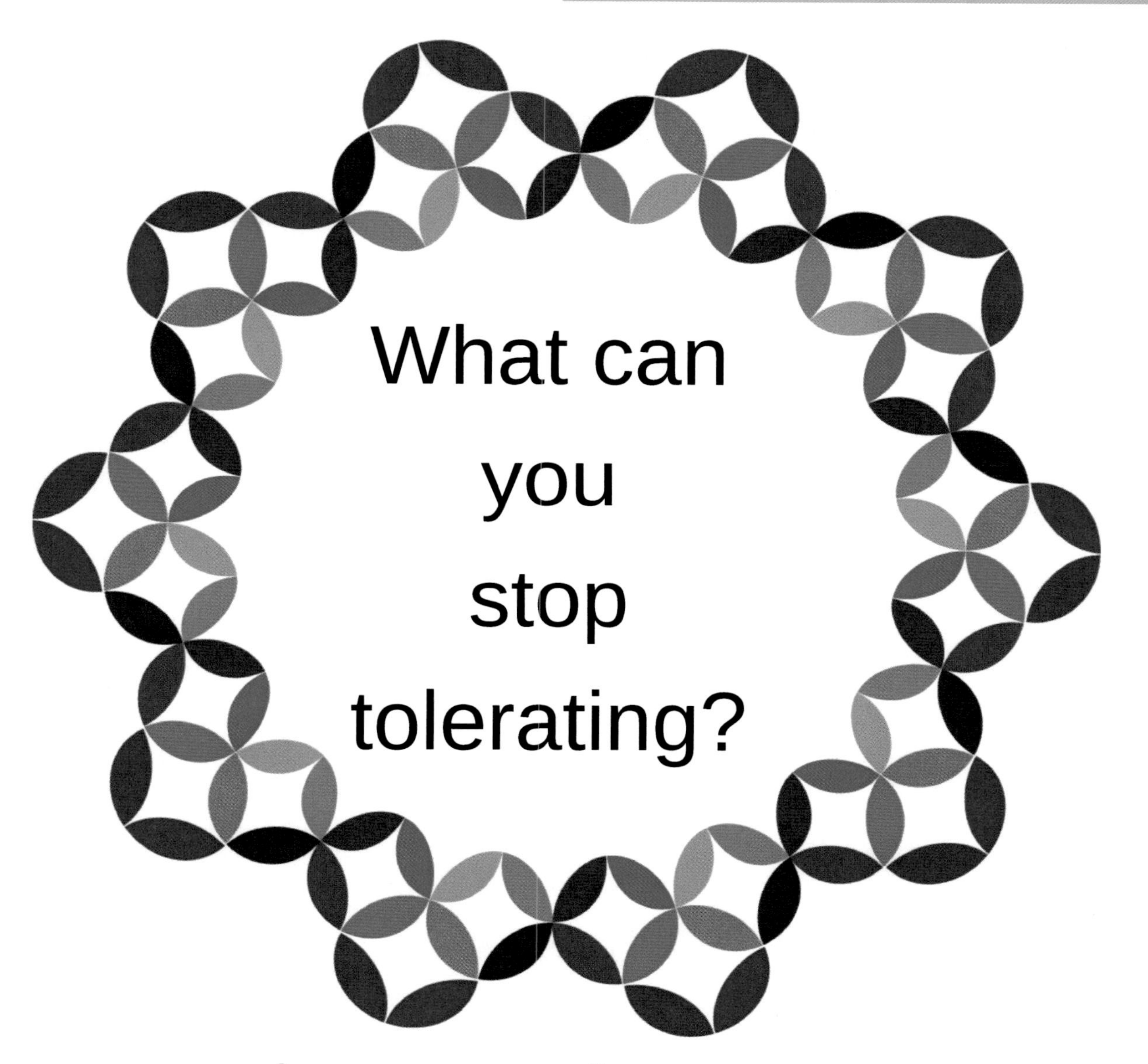

What comes up for you as you reflect on this question?

Capture your thoughts in the notes section.

Notes

M

DIVERSITY BEYOND LIP SERVICE

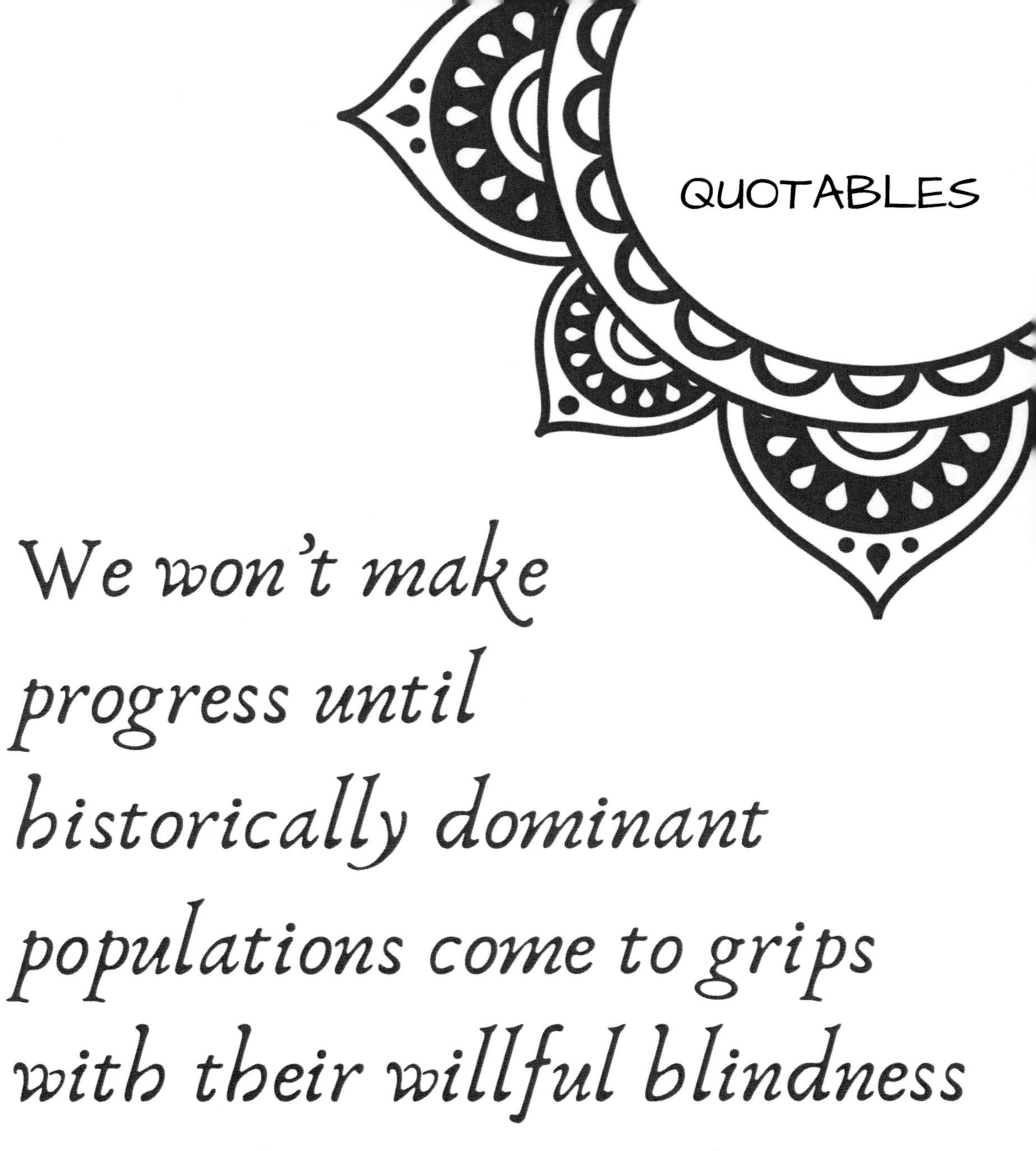

We won't make progress until historically dominant populations come to grips with their willful blindness toward institutional oppression.

The path to inclusion involves **getting comfortable with being uncomfortable.** Society is rightfully calling out the fact that the future success of our organizations demands more diversity. But society can't fix things from the outside. Solutions must come from the organizations themselves, and especially those occupying the C-suite. We must **work from the inside out** to make those in power comfortable with sharing it. There may be some ugly truth uncovered along this path to shared power.

An important note: Some have misinterpreted the call to speak their truth or be authentic to mean that they can say whatever comes to their minds, no matter how offensive.

To be clear, making derogatory remarks about any group regardless of the circumstances only perpetuates prejudice, bias, and exclusion. Moving beyond lip service involves more than just **facing the ugliness of the past** and the privilege of your reality. You must also present behaviors to address and undo their many negative effects.

It is time to acknowledge the **current state** of our **culture** and where it came from. We can't just speak our truth; we have to own it. That latter part is the most important—and the hardest.

Organizations with high-impact coaching programs are more likely to see greater staff engagement and retention, as well as increased revenue.

2014 ICF Global Board Chair Damian Goldvarg, Ph.D., MCC

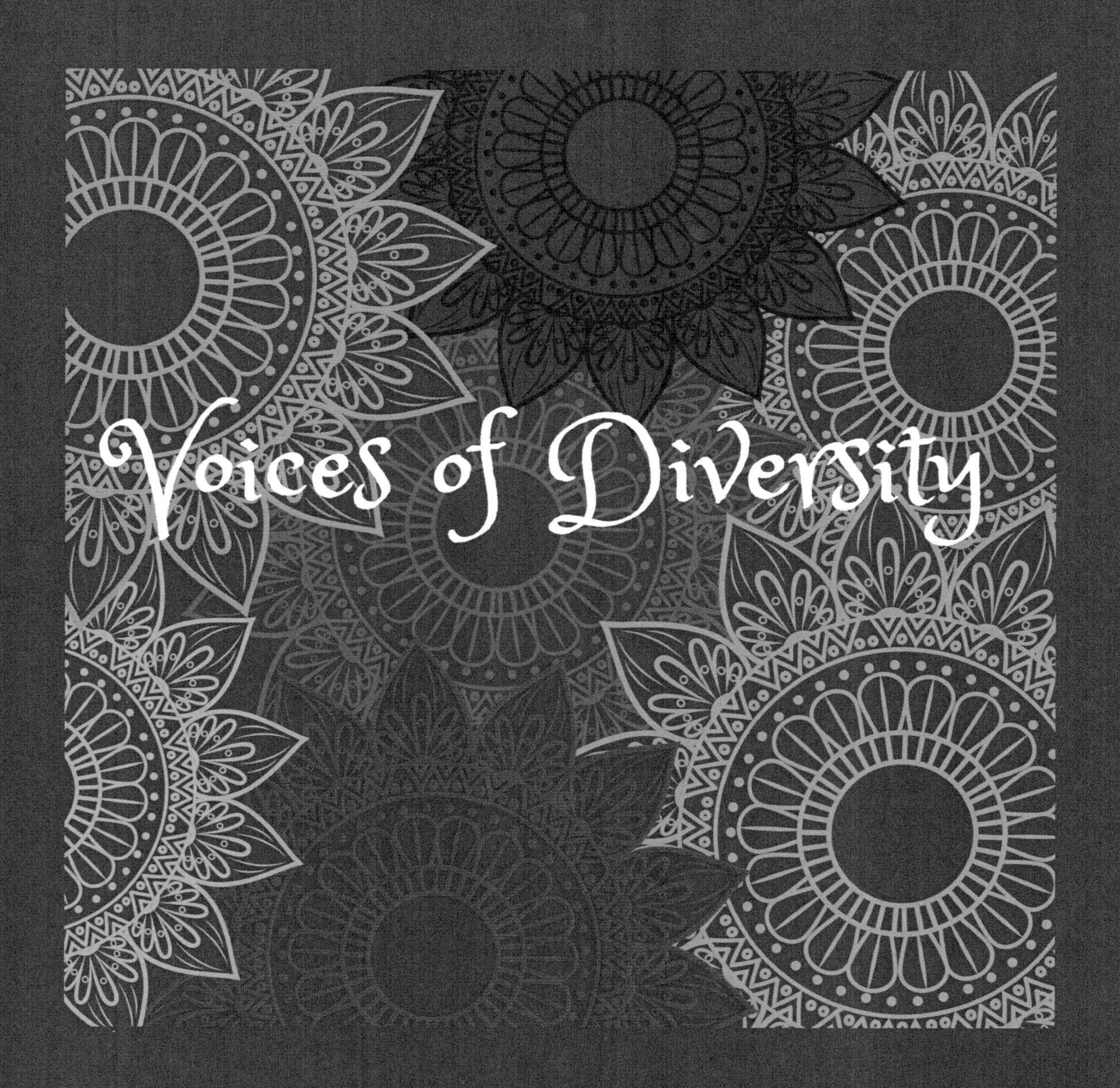
Voices of Diversity

LATINA, FEMALE, CISGENDER - RESPECT

The complexities of many situations we face challenge us to question and **redefine beliefs** we may have previously had that were much simpler. Balancing the desire to take action and speak up for yourself or others with the need to maintain professionalism and anonymity can feel like entering a gray area at times.

There is a difference between knowing something intellectually and understanding it at a visceral level, beyond our own ego or judgment. I've found that at the root of all of the difficult situations I've faced is this: **Everything you wish to see or experience starts with you.** We may not be able to choose all of the situations we find ourselves in, but we can always choose to focus internally and maintain the power to assess with true clarity.

One of the most important things I have and continue to take away from Inclusion Coaching is the incredible power and consequence speaking your truth has on one of the **most invaluable assets** you possess: **your self-respect.** Finding a way to make sure this is honored in a way that feels empowering is one of the most important lessons I continue to learn, in every aspect of my life.

Assessment

RATE EACH STATEMENT USING THE FOLLOWING:

5 Strongly Agree
4 Agree
3 Neutral
2 Disagree
1 Strongly Disagree

I lead by example by using my power and influence to champion diversity and inclusion and encourage my peers to do the same. _______

I help create an environment in which others feel comfortable expressing their wholeness, and no one has to hide a part of him- or herself to “fit in.”

____

I take a collaborative approach and consider diverse ways of learning, working, and leading when setting objectives. _______

I lead with courage and initiate actions or conversations about inclusion at all levels of the managerial hierarchy. ______

I solicit feedback from people with different cultures, backgrounds, and thought processes. I consider ways to better adapt and connect. ______

What are your areas of strength? How have they shown up in your life?

____

____

What are your areas of opportunity? How have they shown up in your life?

____

____

APPLICATION

SELF

- Speak up at meetings and conference calls when exclusionary behaviors show up in decision making.
- Identify the role privilege plays in your work and life and explore how you can use that privilege to lift up others.
- Advocate for diversity and inclusion as core competencies in your organization.

TEAM

- Create a D&I award for your team that rewards inclusive behaviors.
- Develop and implement team diversity and inclusion goals.
- Add a cultural element to your team building activities to engage diverse groups and increase awareness.

BUSINESS

- Audit current D&I activity and remove or adjust any initiatives that are not having an impact on progress.
- Proactively build a pipeline of diverse candidates and work with recruiters to ensure all positions have a diverse slate.
- Invite external D&I thought leaders to address specific business needs with business leaders.

How Will You Coach The Next Generation of Leaders To Commit To Open Their Eyes And Ears?

The COMMIT Model guides coaches in asking individuals empowering questions that tap into their truths and ignite their curiosity about themselves and those who are different from them.

SAMPLE COACHING QUESTIONS:

What do you have that you are not using?

How can you take yourself to the edge and beyond?

What do you choose to take responsibility for, relative to inclusion?

If you were to raise the bar, what would it look like?

What would be possible if you did not censor yourself?

CREATE YOUR OWN COACHING QUESTIONS:

____

____

____

____

____

REFLECTION

How can you harness privilege to empower others?

What comes up for you as you reflect on this question?

Capture your thoughts in the notes section.

Notes

M

DIVERSITY BEYOND LIP SERVICE

QUOTABLES

Inclusion is not about making everyone comfortable. Quite the contrary, inclusion done right will yield productive conflict and controversy.

Naturally, difference in opinions, beliefs, values, and more is also a recipe for conflict—and that can be a good thing!

I believe inclusion done right yields productive conflict and controversy and is the gateway to progress and innovation.

The operative term here is productive. When framed appropriately and addressed with curiosity, conflict can push organizations toward real progress, transforming the insights gleaned from moments of tension into critical steps in building sustainable solutions.

So what does it mean to make room for controversy and conflict in the workplace? It starts with talking about topics and taking actions that have traditionally been considered off limits or taboo. It is acknowledging and accepting that, while ultimately beneficial for all involved, the process will not be easy or comfortable. Encouraging dialogue and corresponding action surrounding controversial issues will require people to move beyond their realm of comfort; it's like a company-wide stretch assignment.

The creation of safe spaces is just the first step in making room for conflict and controversy. The much more difficult part begins once conflict and controversy is embraced, and you are then tasked with taking it to a productive place—before it devolves into chaos.

When you or your employees feel a discussion has reached the point where you need to regroup, a few simple steps can serve as guideposts for reflection and corresponding actions.

First, Pay attention to what is happening without judgment, then Acknowledge your own reactions and interpretations, Understand how others' perceptions differ from yours, Search for common ground to build productive solutions, and finally Execute a mindful and intentional plan. This framework can help you steer things back on course when emotions run high and serve as a launching pad for reengaging in important discussions.

Steps for a Mindful PAUSE

Adapted from Cook Ross

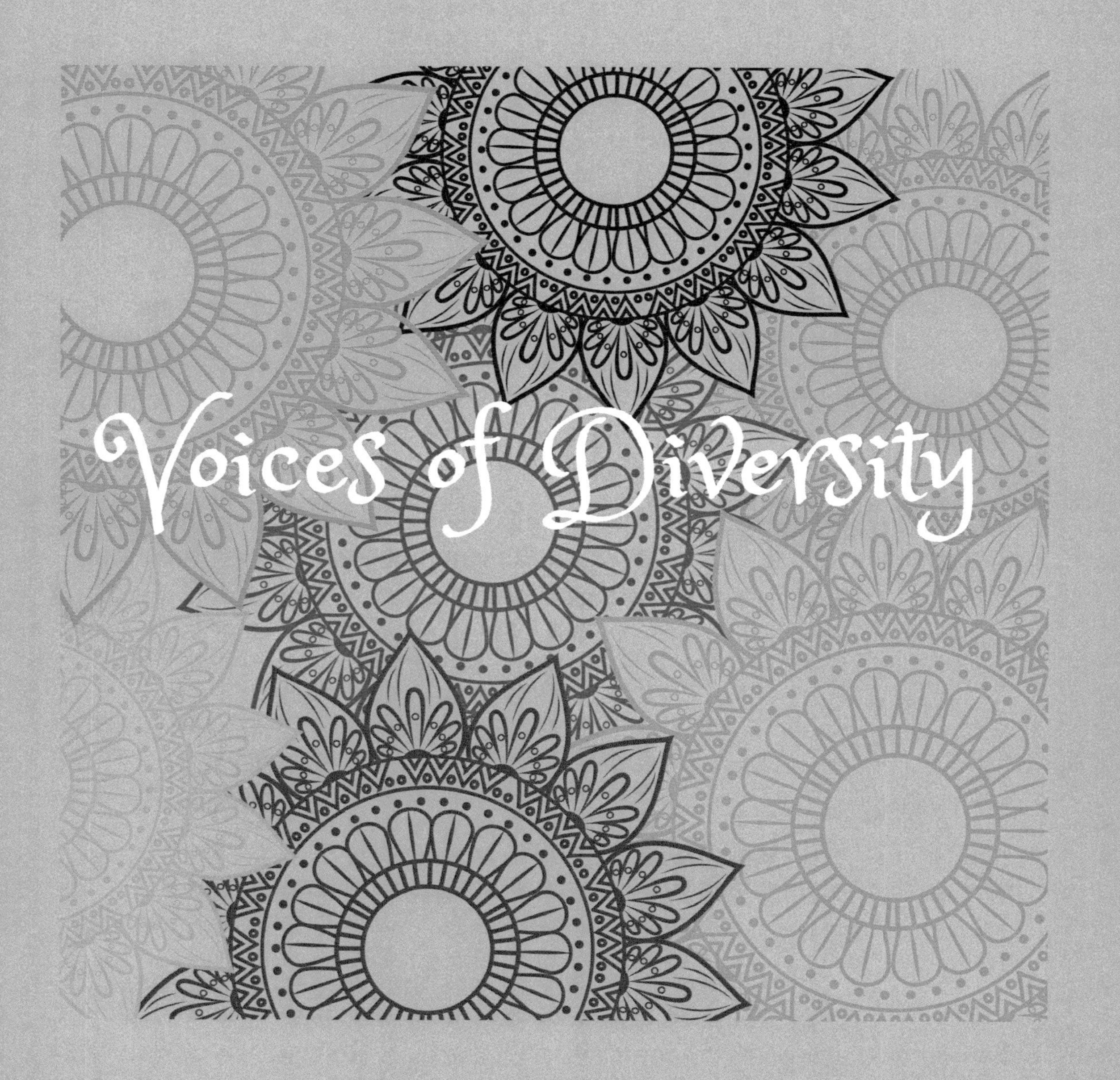
Voices of Diversity

MELANATED, STRAIGHT, MALE - QUESTIONS

Rob McGowan
Transformational Life Coach / Consultant
Diving Within LLC

I am a six-foot-one-inch, highly melanated African-American male who grew up in the heart of Dixie. At the age of forty, while learning meditation and centering practices on the grounds of a former slave plantation in North Carolina, I stood straight up and tall for the first time in over twenty-five years. An incredible alignment and rush of energy knocked me out. If not for a friend who was paying attention, I would've fallen face first onto the gym floor. I was participating in a program for black directors that was focused on self-care practices for those of us working in social justice. After recovering and reflecting a bit, I hurried to my room to share this experience with my mother, who lived in Alabama.

Being mainly raised by a five-foot-ten-inch single mother, I realized that my body carried her fears and anxieties for my safety since I was fourteen, and taller than she was. It wasn't necessarily her words, but more so her frequent looks, questions, and instructions that imparted her worry. I was her only child—the one person she had chosen to conceive, bear, and nurture—yet the realities of the "misfortunes" that befell countless young, melanated males in the South created unforeseen interpersonal dynamics, frequencies, and energies. Not that she wasn't loving, caring, and nurturing, but she was well aware of the infinite possible dangers awaiting me—ones in which I did not have to intentionally engage to be harmed.

MELANATED, STRAIGHT, MALE - QUESTIONS

My experiences growing up and shouldering my mother's concern along with my own, coupled with this training and the tools of a life coach and a corporate consultant, I would like to pose the following set of questions for your consideration:

What does diversity mean to African-American men?

Have they been able to truly benefit from policies and practices focused on diversity?

How do assumptions regarding black male masculinity play out in the workplace?

Why is speaking up or being assertive seen as threatening when it's done by black men, while for others it's seen as ambitious?

What additional hoops or barriers exist for black men in corporate America and worldwide?

How does the percentage of black men in leadership positions reflect the overall talent or competency of black men in business?

How might these issues affect the mental, emotional, psychological, and physical wellbeing of black men, particularly when there are few outlets to effectively emote in the workplace?

If you've never thought about most of these, or questions like them, there may be some issues surrounding diversity playing out for the African-American males in your workplace.

Assessment

RATE EACH STATEMENT USING THE FOLLOWING:

5 Strongly Agree
4 Agree
3 Neutral
2 Disagree
1 Strongly Disagree

I consistently honor my values when faced with difficult or sensitive topics.

____

I approach conflict with humility and vulnerability, and remain open to new information and insights. _______

I say no to requests that marginalize or exclude others. _______

I encourage accountability for inclusion at my organization—from every individual, at every level, every day. ______

I lean into my fear and discomfort when faced with challenging situations.

______

What are your areas of strength? How have they shown up in your life?

____

____

What are your areas of opportunity? How have they shown up in your life?

____

____

APPLICATION

SELF

- Identify your D&I triggers and create a mental exercise to activate when needed.
- Be intentional about not avoiding tough conversations.
- Recruit someone who has very different views from you to join your team.

TEAM

- Share your positive experiences with working through conflict relative to differences.
- Create multiple avenues for your team to communicate unpopular news or concerns, i.e. written, anonymous, verbal, individually, or as a team
- Introduce and practice the PAUSE method at team meetings.

BUSINESS

- Establish safe spaces that allow people to share their experiences and speak their truths relative to D&I.
- Solicit and offer alternative solutions when communicating difficult business decisions.
- Develop a social plan as a companion to your business plan to show empathy for the human impact of tough discussions.

How Will You Coach The Next Generation of Leaders To Commit To Make Room for Controversy and Conflict?

The COMMIT Model guides coaches in asking individuals empowering questions that tap into their truths and ignite their curiosity about themselves and those who are different from them.

SAMPLE COACHING QUESTIONS:

What would the best version of you choose to do next?

What scares you about diversity and inclusion?

What can you say no to?

What's stopping you?

What would it cost you if things remained the same as they are?

CREATE YOUR OWN COACHING QUESTIONS:

____

____

____

____

____

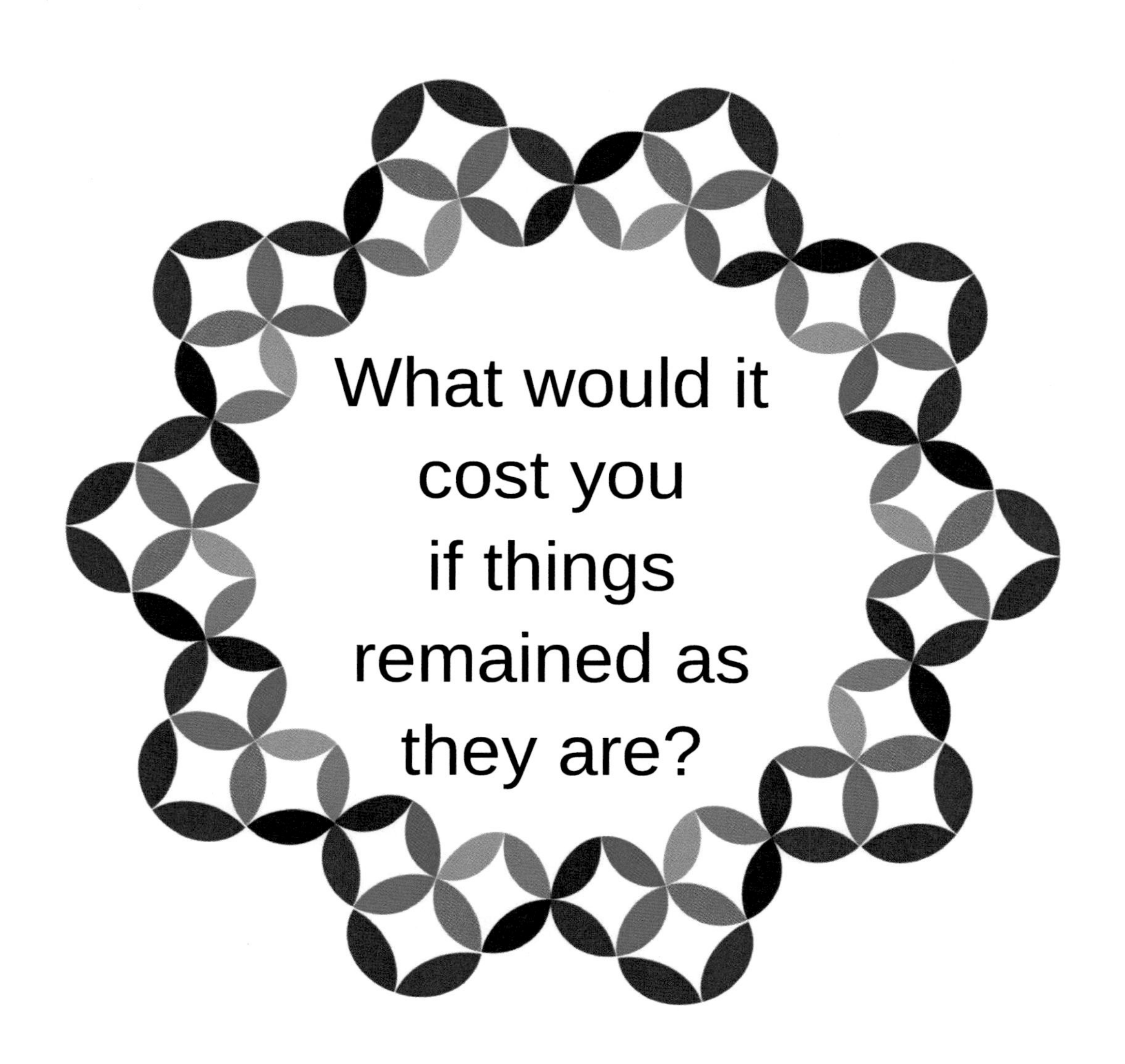

What comes up for you as you reflect on this question?

Capture your thoughts in the notes section.

Notes

DIVERSITY BEYOND LIP SERVICE

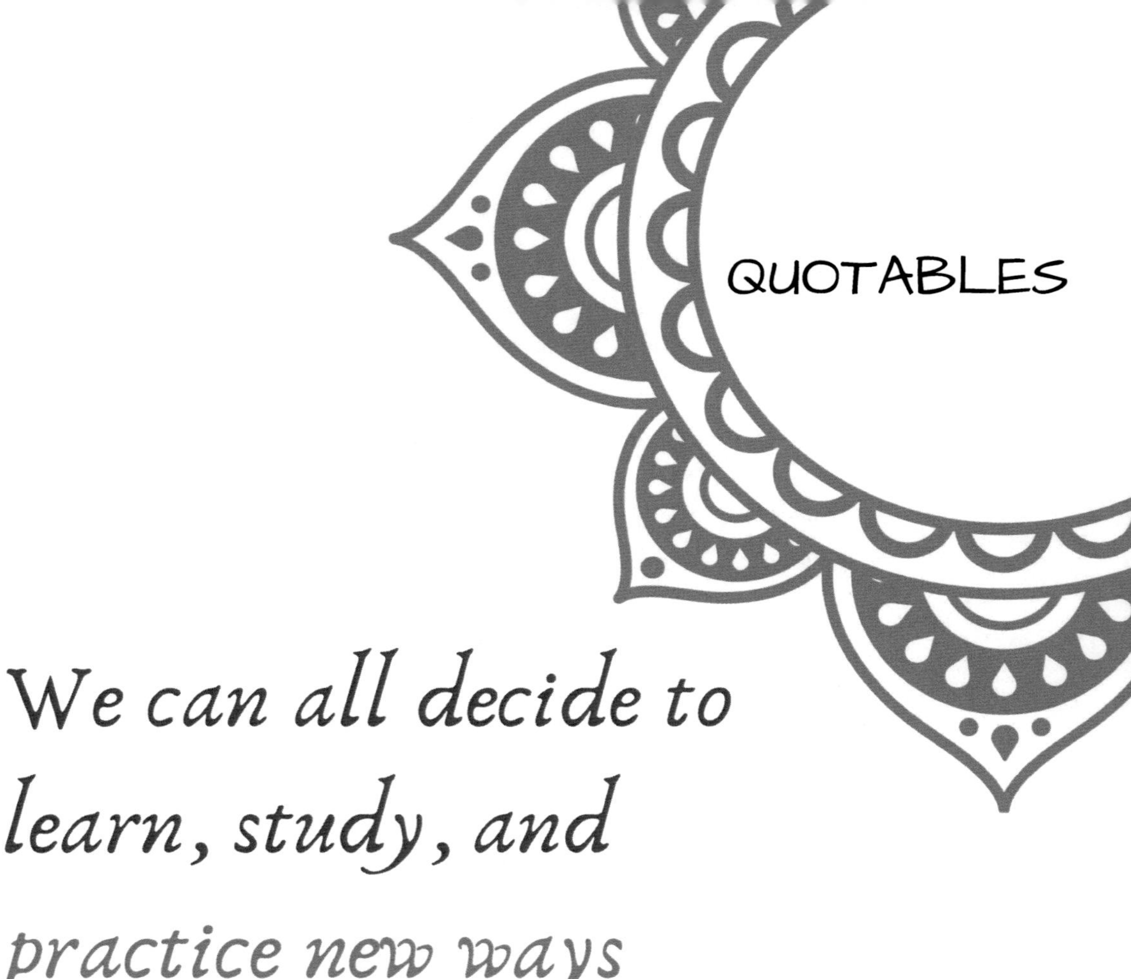

We can all decide to
learn, study, and
practice new ways
of thinking and doing
that help us
change our behavior.

ENGAGE

Every employee is valuable human capital, and it is the responsibility of an organization and its leadership to maximize each individual's potential and contributions. Getting the most out of those we work with means **changing the frame of the conversation** and creating an environment in which everyone feels comfortable enough to contribute their unique perspectives—even when those ideas conflict with popular opinions.

We need people to put out new ideas, others to challenge them, and still others to address them from a different angle. Different voices, different experiential backgrounds, and different ways of thinking are how we **find ways to tap into new markets and expand our businesses.** They help us understand why something we are doing today may not be working and offer new ways of operating that could be much more effective.

Voices of Diversity

STRAIGHT, WHITE, MALE, VETERAN - ROB

Rob was very serious when he came to his coaching session. "I just don't understand what I need to do," he said. "I'm doing my best work, but it feels like my best is never good enough."

I nodded. "I can hear the frustration in your voice."

"I usually don't share my veteran status at work because it sets some people off, but it makes me mad to have to hide the fact that I put my life on the line for my country."

I responded, "I'm so sorry that you've been made to feel that way. Thank you for your service."

Rob looked down at his hands and continued. "I came to this company because they advertised themselves as being 'military friendly.' Now that I'm here, it feels like they were just trying to put on a good show by hiring a few veterans. This is not what I signed up for."

"What do you need most right now?" I asked.

Rob thought for a moment. "Respect. I want my manager and my colleagues to respect me and the value I bring to the organization, based on my own merit and nothing else. I feel like my manager is constantly 'handling me'—like she and some of my colleagues assume that all veterans have PTSD. She never gives me real feedback. She acts like she's afraid that I may lose it or something if she gives me constructive criticism. I see it in some of my peers, too. They'll say they respect my service, but they also act a little distant, like they don't know how to take me."

"So what's most important to you about respect?"

"I just want people to respect me enough to be able to tell me like it is. If my work is great, say that. If I need to step it up, tell me. And most important, if I need a good kick in the rear to get things moving, I need to hear that, too. I wish they'd just give it to me straight; I can take it."

How would you coach Rob if you were his manager?

How would you coach Rob's manager if she was a member of your team?

What's one coaching question that you would use for each of them to help them invite new perspectives?

Rob's situation also highlights the need to further explore and understand **intersectionality**—the overlap of various aspects of our identities. People don't just represent one type of diversity. Rob is white, male, heterosexual, and a veteran. While on the surface it may seem as if he is simply part of the dominant majority, his story is more complex, and the aspects of Rob's identity that make him different are also the ones that he can harness to add more value to an organization.

INTERSECTIONALITY

Each of us have our own unique mix of intersectionality
Circle all that resonate with or apply to you.

A VETERAN

divorced

Gender Neutral

1st Generation College Graduate

Single Parent

EXTROVERT

An Immigrant

Multi-racial

Christian

middle class

Millennial

Able-Bodied

Asian/Pacific Islander

TRANS

Lesbian

Buddhist

I AM

Refugee

White

Cisgender

Male

Hindu

Multilingual

Single

AFRICAN DESCENT/ BLACK

Baby Boomer

GAY

Gen X

Muslim

Straight

Working Class

FEMALE

Adoptive Parent

A person with a disability

Atheist

Married

____

____

____

All of our identities, history, and being show up at the same time.
It's time we recognize and appreciate that we are all multi-faceted beings who can't be confined to a single story.

Assessment

RATE EACH STATEMENT USING THE FOLLOWING:

5 Strongly Agree
4 Agree
3 Neutral
2 Disagree
1 Strongly Disagree

I seek to learn about cultures and backgrounds different from my own.

____

I see every day as an opportunity to meet new people and learn more about my colleagues. _______

I remain open to possibilities by constantly asking, “What else is possible?”

____

I invite opposing thoughts and ideas when making decisions. ______

I ask open-ended questions to gain broader perspectives. ______

What are your areas of strength? How have they shown up in your life?

____

____

What are your areas of opportunity? How have they shown up in your life?

____

____

APPLICATION

SELF

- Proactively seek feedback from colleagues that are different from you to uncover any cultural blindspots.
- Become intentional about understanding the experience of non-majority employees.
- Reflect on your "circles." What voices are muted in your professional and personal life? What voices do you need to include?

TEAM

- Prioritize hiring candidates who bring new perspectives and add a new dimension to your team when making hiring decisions.
- Utilize your team to curate and share D&I content relevant to your business with the team and on internal networks.
- Invite people to share their D&I stories: Where are they from? How do they identify? What have been their experiences with inclusion or exclusion?

BUSINESS

- Get out into communities and serve! Engage with your customers to better understand their needs through social responsibility initiatives.
- Host "Innovation Challenge" meetings with cross-functional partners and ensure a diversity of voices are around the table to brainstorm new ways of working and business opportunities.
- Facilitate Inclusion Circles using the Inclusion Circle Card deck. (see Additional Resources section).

How Will You Coach The Next Generation of Leaders To Commit To Invite New Perspectives?

The COMMIT Model guides coaches in asking individuals empowering questions that tap into their truths and ignite their curiosity about themselves and those who are different from them.

SAMPLE COACHING QUESTIONS:

Who are you becoming?

What is emerging?

What's possible?

What are your choices?

What will you do to stay aware of others' perspectives?

CREATE YOUR OWN COACHING QUESTIONS:

____

____

____

____

____

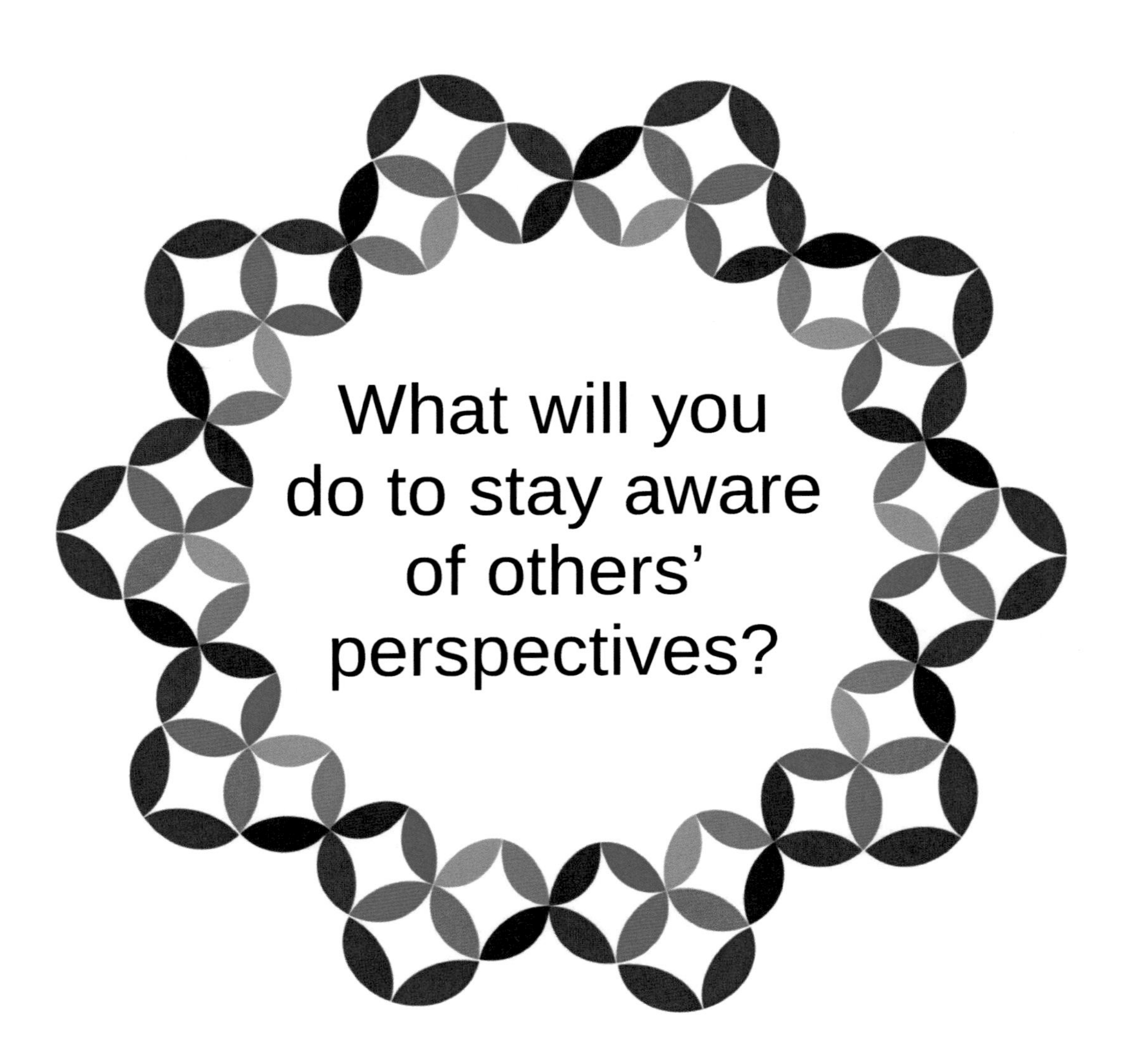

What comes up for you as you reflect on this question?

Capture your thoughts in the notes section.

Notes

T

DIVERSITY BEYOND LIP SERVICE

I'm not concerned
about the truth
that makes me free;
I'm in pursuit
of the truth
that makes us all free.

You know your team would be even stronger if it were more diverse, or if the diversity you do have were better utilized, so why don't you want to rock the boat? What is the "why" hiding behind your reasons for not acting?

What story are you telling yourself about why it's better to keep quiet? What truth should you share instead? This is the kind of self-reflection that will eventually empower you to speak up and move the diversity and inclusion conversation forward.

Honing the skills to diagnose your own attempts at self-deception, as well as others'—and seek out truth instead—may be tiresome, uncomfortable, or even painful, but it's essential when promoting diversity, equality, and inclusion. This will require a level of radical truth and vulnerability that we have yet to achieve—but it's possible.

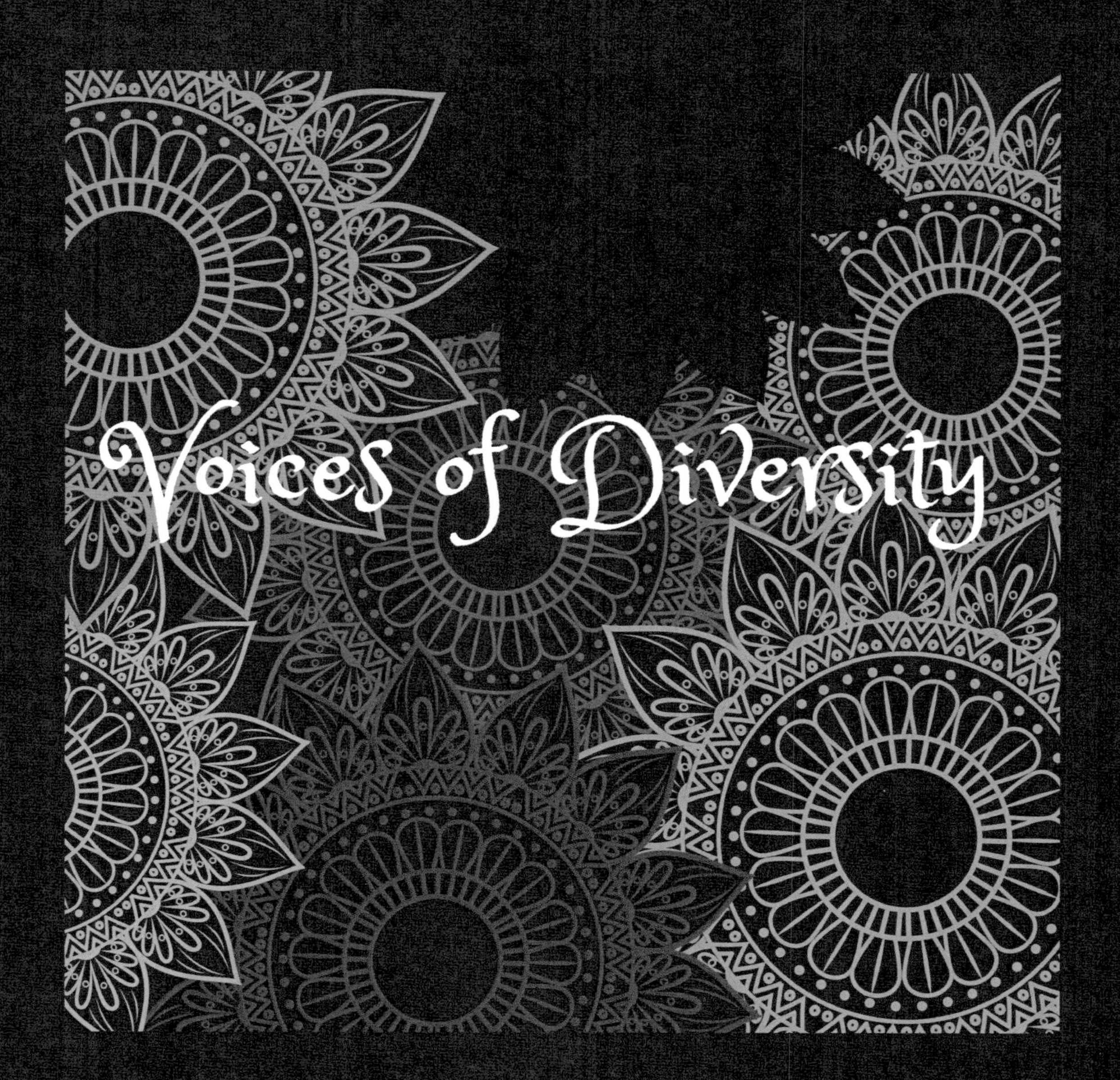
Voices of Diversity

LISTEN

NON-BINARY, ABLE-BODIED 1ST GENERATION COLLEGE GRADUATE

Our society is built on systems and structures that label and categorize everything. We've even begun to categorize folks who **don't wish to be categorized!** It's a part of how we make sense of the world around us. However, we often choose a single sliver of our being to prioritize above all others. Then, we select a few other identities that we keep in our minds at all times. All of this leads to the belief that these things make up who we are and determine how we show up.

For example, after coming out, most people move through the world as a newly out person for a while. Everything is centered on this freshly revealed aspect of their identity. However, the reality is that all of their identities, **all of their history, and all of their being show up at the same time.** Here's how all of these factors play out for me.

Following my coming out, I felt an immediate difference. **Social interactions were strained**, normal office talk was somehow more complicated, even my personal goals and aspirations were affected. I found this particularly interesting because I'd heard a number of people express their comfort and openness to people of different sexual orientations.

However, I've come to realize that while people are comfortable with quiet, agreeable social outliers, they don't like loud, confrontational ones. On some level, the folks around me had decided that since **I wasn't a part of the norm**, I shouldn't show up and demand to take up space the same way others did. I was not expected to talk about things specific to gay culture unless it was in the cute, sideshow-style, anecdotal way that other people found amusing. Rarely do these well-intended but empty gestures turn into policy changes that shift an organization's culture.

If you want queer people to work for your organization, you must do the work of creating a sense of belonging for them.

If your organization is **unaware** of the impact and reach **of systemic oppression**, it is undoubtedly participating in the perpetuation of that oppression.
This is where our discussions must begin from now on.

Assessment

RATE EACH STATEMENT USING THE FOLLOWING:

5 Strongly Agree
4 Agree
3 Neutral
2 Disagree
1 Strongly Disagree

I am comfortable articulating the value of inclusion for my organization and for myself. _______

I ensure that all voices are included when setting goals and building action plans. _______

I take a collaborative approach and consider diverse ways of learning, working, and leading when setting objectives. _______

I apply a D&I lens when identifying and evaluating key metrics, including qualitative and quantitative data. ______

I consider the cultural and global impact on my team, organization, and society when making decisions. ______

What are your areas of strength? How have they shown up in your life?

____

____

What are your areas of opportunity? How have they shown up in your life?

____

____

APPLICATION

SELF

- Explore your internal dialogue about D&I, own where you are in your journey, and share your truth.
- Develop self-management practices such as journaling and physical activity to handle your D&I triggers.
- Take a hard look at the "why" behind your biases and reasons for not doing more to further diversity and inclusion.

TEAM

- Add "Share Your Truth" sessions to your one-on-one meetings with your team. Allow for open discussion where you are simply trying to understand and learn about their needs.
- Establish ground rules for team interactions and meetings that allow for honest feedback without fear of judgment or retaliation.
- Host an Inclusion Circle using the Inclusion Card Deck when the truth is hard to hear or accept relative to your team or business (see Additional Resources).

BUSINESS

- Share research, articles, books, and TED talks that demonstrate linkages between your business imperatives and D&I.
- Partner with external associations that are serving diverse demographics to help increase organizational and industry D&I.
- Pushback on policies that perpetuate the status quo relative to D&I.

How Will You Coach The Next Generation of Leaders To Commit To Tell the Truth Even When It Hurts?

The COMMIT Model guides coaches in asking individuals empowering questions that tap into their truths and ignite their curiosity about themselves and those who are different from them.

SAMPLE COACHING QUESTIONS:

What do you care about in this situation?

When you talk to yourself about yourself, what do you say?

What truth would you like to share?

How does inclusivity honor your values?

What story do you tell yourself about people whose culture differs from yours?

CREATE YOUR OWN COACHING QUESTIONS:

____

____

____

____

____

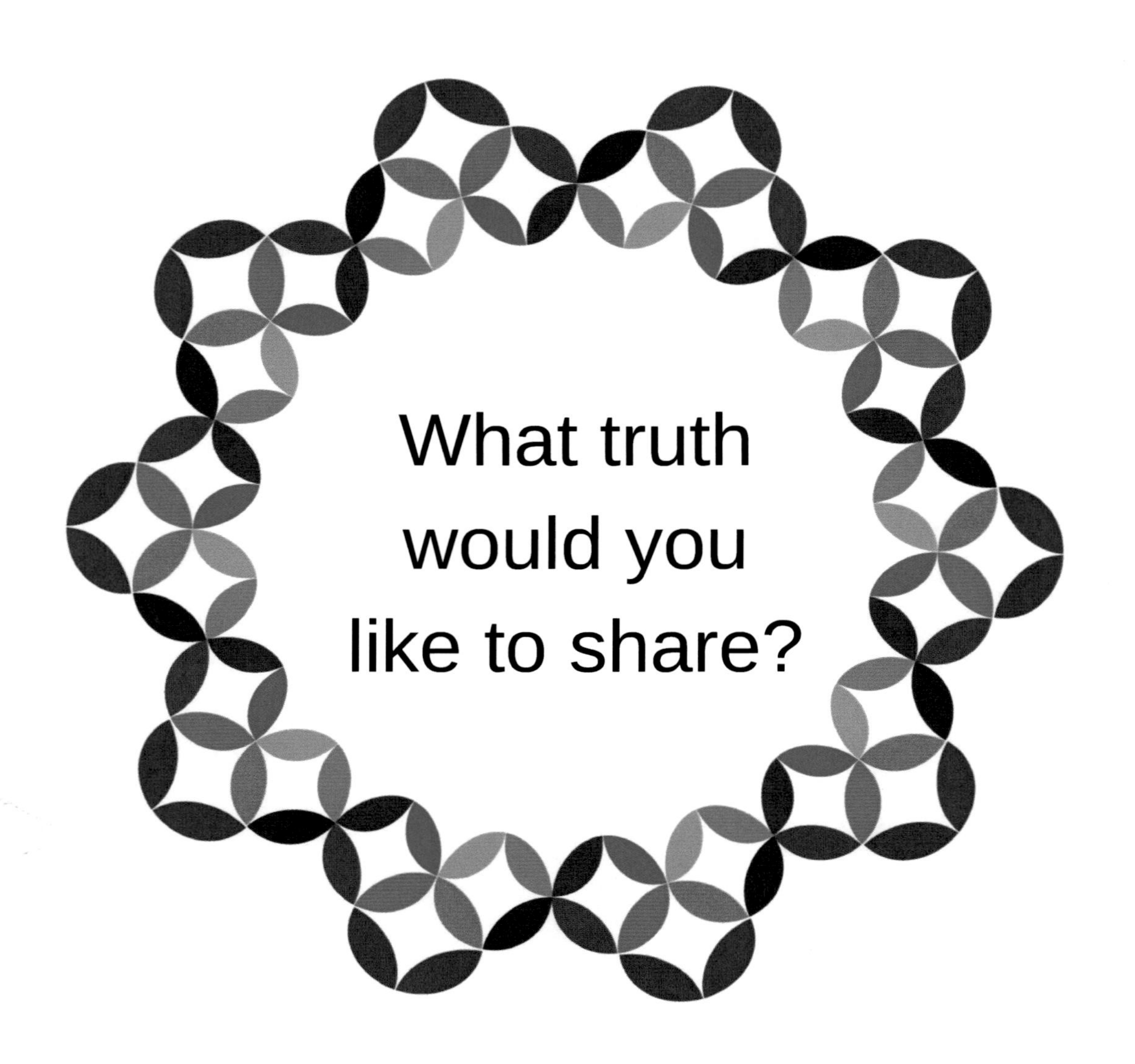

What comes up for you as you reflect on this question?
Capture your thoughts in the notes section.

REFORM

It's your responsibility to **reimagine and redesign** your organization to create an inclusive environment for all of your employees. We must go beyond simple "inclusion" work and venture into the work that **reforms and disrupts**.

To do this, we must ask some tough questions:

- How might our policies be complicit in systems of oppression?
- Whom do our policies benefit most and why?
- What can I reimagine about my business to create a more versatile experience that fits the needs of all my employees?
- How might our professional expectations be discriminatory toward certain groups of people?
- How can we create opportunities for marginalized groups to thrive?
- How can we affirm people's true identities—beyond their utility at work?

Notes

PING

Ping came to a coaching session visibly frustrated with her career progress. She had been a stellar performer on her company's operations team for eight years, but her dissatisfaction with her job responsibilities was beginning to affect her performance.

"I want to explore a career switch to a sales or marketing position where I could better leverage my creative talent, but everyone tells me I need to stay in operations. I also want to work in a customer-facing role where I can interact with people on a regular basis."

She paused for a few seconds before adding, "I think they believe I am only suited for operations roles because I am Asian."

Both Ping's mentor and her HR representative had told her that they saw her continuing in an operations role focused on metrics and analytics. Her previous manager had also made comments that her heavy accent made her somewhat ill-suited for customer-facing positions.

SCENARIO

With the six COMMIT steps in mind, how might you coach Ping in her situation? How can you create a safe space for exploration? What culturally aware and empowering questions could you ask Ping?

COMMIT TO COURAGEOUS ACTION

Ping has already touched on one of the questions in the "C" column of COMMIT: **What contribution or difference do you want to make?**

She is interested in using her creative talents to enhance either the sales or marketing at her company. Perhaps you might ask her to delve deeper into how she'd like to contribute, or follow up by asking about what success looks like to her. What would her ideal career life look like one, five, or even ten years down the line? How exactly does she see herself contributing, and what kind of environment would she need to reach her full potential?

OPEN YOUR EYES AND EARS

You may ask Ping, *What does it feel like to be excluded?* Listening to her answer and getting a taste of the true impact—personally and professionally—of the feedback Ping has received could help Ping and her manager understand what she is experiencing and take steps to make changes, both for Ping's sake and the sake of her organization.

Another question that may help Ping progress is, *What can you stop tolerating?* Are there ways that Ping can advocate for herself by refusing to accept others' limits on her growth? This question is not meant to put the burden on Ping to shift any biases her manager and HR department may have—or those embedded within her organization, for that matter. Instead, it is meant to give her the agency to explore any factors that may be holding her back and empower her to make the moves necessary to advance her career.

SCENARIO

MOVE BEYOND LIP SERVICE

Next, you can ask Ping: **What do you have that you are not using?** The answer to this question could take a variety of forms. Ping may realize that she has professional contacts, access to classes or trainings, or any number of other resources that could help her make the switch to a more creative role at her organization or elsewhere, if necessary.

MAKE ROOM FOR CONTROVERSY AND CONFLICT

You can support Ping in “making room for controversy and conflict” by asking, What would it cost you if things remained the same? Would it affect her happiness, her income, or any other aspect of her personal or professional life? And is that a cost she’s willing to incur?

INVITE NEW PERSPECTIVES

Considering what's at stake, it's time to for Ping to explore **What is possible?** Often, this question is pretty motivating. With an idea of what she could achieve, Ping can take the steps to make it a reality.

TELL THE TRUTH EVEN WHEN IT HURTS

Finally, you can ask Ping, **What truth do you want to share?** Ping can explore her situation and what she wants to happen with her mentor, as well as HR and any other relevant stakeholders. She can explain her thoughts, feelings, and concerns regarding the situation, as well as the ways in which she feels she can better contribute and meet her own aspirations in a different role within the organization.

With Ping's insights—and the COMMIT™ model in mind—all parties can move beyond lip service and reach the heart of the matter.

As you set off on the next stage of your own D&I journey, use the following commitment statement to reinforce your thoughts, your actions, and—most important—your ongoing commitment to advancing diversity, equity, inclusion, and belonging in work and life:

I commit to courageous action, doing my **best to cultivate an inclusive environment** for myself, my team, my organization, and my industry.

I commit to opening my eyes and ears to the good, the bad, and the ugly, and to taking steps to **champion the good and change the bad and ugly** circumstances that hold us all back.

I commit to moving beyond lip service, making sure that **I "walk the talk"** when it comes to diversity, equity, inclusion, and belonging.

I commit to making room for controversy and conflict, with the knowledge that it is only when these moments of friction occur that we can **transform and transcend together.**

I commit to inviting new perspectives by **seeking** the insight of a **diversity of voices**, which always adds value.

I commit to **telling the truth**, even when it hurts, to challenge bias, remove barriers, and **make meaningful progress.**

Most of all, **I commit** to the **continuous pursuit** of diversity, equity, inclusion, and belonging with the goal of creating a **better workplace and society for all.**

About the Author

An inspirational leader and dynamic facilitator, La'Wana Harris is a Certified Diversity Executive, an ICF Credentialed Coach, and a global leadership development professional who has dedicated her career to aligning performance with business strategy. She has demonstrated success across a broad range of corporate functions, including global leadership and organizational development, diversity and inclusion, government affairs, and market access. In addition, as a community activist she has created diversity and inclusion awareness programs and designed overall integrated management solutions.

La'Wana is driven by a firm belief in honoring and speaking the truth, no matter how challenging that may be. As a result, she's recognized throughout the leadership community as someone gifted in sparking meaningful and insightful dialogue that ultimately inspires change.

Throughout the decades of her professional career and social justice activism, La'Wana has received numerous industry and community awards. Most recently, she was recognized as one of 2018's 100 Most Inspiring People in the life-sciences industry by PharmaVOICE magazine. She also received the Women in Leadership award from the National Black MBA Association and was invited to join the Forbes Coaches Council as a contributor and thought leader.

La'Wana is also a respected humanitarian and philanthropist. Understanding how important it is for children to read books with characters they can relate to, she created two book series featuring children of color. These books promote cultural diversity and are translated in the native languages of underserved nations. La'Wana has donated 10,000 books in Haitian Creole to schools and orphanages in partnership with Grace International. Through her efforts, U.S. sales from these books help support young females entering careers in STEM.

To learn more about La'Wana and engage in the important work of advancing diversity and inclusion, visit **lawanaharris.com**.

Contact:
coachlawana@gmail.com

ADDITIONAL RESOURCES:

Diversity Beyond Lip Service: A Coaching Guide for Challenging Bias

The elephant in the room with diversity work is that people with privilege must use it to allow others equal access to power. This is often why diversity efforts falter--people believe in diversity until they feel that they have to give something up. How do we talk them through this shift?

Knowing where to start with authentic dialogue about D&I issues can be a challenge for many leaders.

The Inclusion Circle™ card deck is an effective tool to get meaningful conversation started in an engaging format. Empower your leaders to create a non-judgmental, safe space with simple instructions to allow for greater connection with intact and cross-functional teams.

ADDITIONAL RESOURCES:

GLOBAL DIVERSITY AND INCLUSION BENCHMARKS:

Standards for Organizations Around the World (or for short, the GDIB). The GDIB helps organizations determine strategy and measure progress in managing diversity and fostering inclusion. It is a free downloadable 80-page booklet that can be used by submitting the Permission Agreement. The GDIB was written by its co-authors and The Centre's founding board members Julie O'Mara, Board Chair and President, Alan Richter, Ph.D., Treasurer, and 95 Expert Panelists.

centreforglobalinclusion.org

INCLUSION NUDGES:

People in this Inclusion Nudges community empower and enable each other to increase inclusion by sharing their nudges for inclusion. This non-profit global initiative is free for all and provides equal access for all.

http://inclusion-nudges.org

ADDITIONAL RESOURCES:

available at

lawanaharris.com

#iCOMMIT

Made in the USA
Monee, IL
03 February 2021